OTHER BOOKS BY GEORGE MENDOZA

Allegories

AND AMEDEO ASKED, HOW DOES ONE BECOME A MAN?
THE PUMA AND THE PEARL
A PIECE OF STRING
THE HUNTER, THE TICK AND THE GUMBEROO
FLOWERS AND GRASSES AND WEEDS
THE PRACTICAL MAN
THE HAWK IS HUMMING, a novel
HUNTING SKETCHES, short stories
THE WORLD FROM MY WINDOW

Poetry

THE HUNTER I MIGHT HAVE BEEN
THE SAND POEMS
TO SEE A TRAIN GO BY
AND I MUST HURRY FOR THE SEA IS COMING IN
FISH IN THE SKY
PEBBLES IN THE GRASS
A POEM FOR PUTTING TO SEA

And Books for All Ages

HERMAN'S HAT
GWOT! HORRIBLY FUNNY HAIRTICKLERS
THE CRACK IN THE WALL
THE GILLYGOOFANG
A WART SNAKE IN A FIG TREE
THE BEASTLY ALPHABET BOOK
THE DIGGER WASP
THE CATERPILLAR MAN
THE GOOD LUCK SPIDER

THE STARFISH TRILOGY

THE
STARFISH
TRILOGY

by George Mendoza
illustrated by Ati Forberg

Funk & Wagnalls
New York

FOR KEENE . . .

"Ah, were life but straight
how we'd live it then.
But it's fated otherwise
you have to turn in a small corner."

(GEORGE SEFERIS)

TO
SPIN
A SILKEN
LINE
OR
TWO

Along the cool morning dew, along the cool forest floor crept a spider, a shabby little thing of a spider, looking for a place to spin a silken line or two.

Over speckled fishlike skins of leaves he crept, over earth-soft mossy pads, over turtle still adream, earth-anchored in its shell, over bogs of stones and crackling twigs he crept, crept on and on, seeking a place to spin a silken line or two.

When he was hungry, the little spider would hunt and kill an ant or two, but never more than he had need to eat. He was not a weaver of webs-in-waiting for bugs and flies to be caught in sticky shrouds of morning jewels.

11

He came only to find a place where he might spin a silken line or two.

He crawled till noon, till the bright noon sun came through the tops of the trees like golden ringlets sparkling on the starry leaves, till the forest floor was all a sea of dewy crystals flashing to the sky and all the leaves were sails that wanted to fly.

He stopped and looked high up and saw the many silken webs strung to sift the sun, bough to bough they hung, some high, some low, so many bugs and flies stuck to webs that caught them long ago.

Here I'll stay, the little spider thought, to spin a silken line or two. One line will take me to a far-off leaf where I may sometime sleep and another as high as I can go.

Thereupon he set himself a silken line to reach that distant leaf when soon there came a spider, a black bushy spider, legs dangling from a far flung web.

14

"You have picked a choice place to spin your web," cried the bushy spider. "As you can see there are bugs and flies more than one can eat."

"I am not a weaver of webs," said the little spider. "As you can see I spin a line only to reach a leaf."

"And tomorrow, what will you eat tomorrow?"

"Tomorrow," said the little spider, "I will spin tomorrow a silken line as high as I can go."

"What is a spider without a web? Where will you go? Where will you go?"

16

"Perhaps to spin among the stars," said the shabby spider. "Perhaps to spin among the frosty stars my silken line will go."

"And will you drop a silken hook to earth for an ant or bug? When it comes time to eat you will weep, little spider, and you will know, only too late you will know."

But the little spider was curled asleep with the moon upon his leaf. He had still tomorrow, you know, a silken line to spin as high as he could go. 17

THE KING WHO LIVED IN THE EARTH

20

Once there was a king who was an ant. He was
a greedy king and he lived in a hole in the
ground where it was always very cool. Down
deep in the cool earth he stayed without ever
going out of his hole. When he was hungry
he would send out an army of ants. But when
he was very hungry he would send out each ant
to the last number to fetch and carry bits and
crumbs for he was a king who never went
without. 21

Swarming out of the cool ground into the hot sun, the ants would scurry about trying to find food for their king. All day they would lift and carry, lift and carry, while the hot sun blazed upon their bones.

So many, many did not come back.

As their numbers became smaller and smaller, a voice among the weary rose up, a dried-up, dust-choked ant:

"Why is it so hot? All day always so hot!"

And all the ants began to wail into the blazing noon:

"There he sits, our greedy king, in the cool earth under, while the hot red sun makes our bones thunder!"

23

"Let us find another!"

"He would have us fetch and carry till our dust fills the cracks of stones!"

"Let us find another!"

"He grows fat, each day so fat, while our scorched skins serve his fancy!"

And all the ants together boiled in their bones:

"What can we do!"

"Kill him!" came a fiery cry.

"There he sits in the cool earth under, while we are like coals fed to the furnace of the sun!"

"What can we do! What can we do!"

And all the ants began to chant:

"Kill him! Kill him! Kill him!"

But there was among the many, an ant who thought not once but twice and sometimes three times over.

"Can you not remember? He is still our king. While we are but the many."

"How many . . . look how many!" moaned a bony ant.

25

"If the king tells us to lift the sun, it is for us to do and lift the sun," said the wise ant to the withered and the weary. "If he tells us to go hungry that we should feed him till his thirst is done, it is for us to do and well it should be done. All together we should haul and haul together."

"My back aches! My bones quake!" cried a weed of an ant. "His thirst is never done. While he sits in the cool earth under, my belly grows weak and numb!"

"Stake him to the ground and burn him!" cried an ant, frantically running around in circles.

"Let him gloat in all his splendor," said the wise ant. "Let him, if he will, take even one of us to eat! But let us rake the field and turn each tiny stone, let us grub over ground and stubble, in all our numbers, let us haul, haul together so that our king grows fat, round and fat, in his cool hole under."

27

Across the field they went forth in all their weary numbers to please their greedy king. Each time fewer and fewer came back, each time their king grew and grew, puffed with fat.

Until one day no ant came to fetch and carry for the king whose thirst was never done. And the king alas so mighty that he could not move, was trapped for all his days to come in the cool earth under.

29

THE
SLEEPING
SEED

The seed in the ground lay sleeping, sleeping in the ground. It was round and small like a pebble and inside it was sleeping, sleeping in the ground.

All around it was the earth, black and hard and deep, and the seed was the seed of a flower, sleeping, sleeping in the ground. 33

Now this night it did start breathing a fiery, fiery glow, for down deep under it was stirring, stirring in the ground.

It could not see the million floating stars or the gold, gold moon sinking down the sea, or hear the lone night cricket coming every now and then. And yet, it was stirring, all the time stirring, stirring in the ground. 35

It could not see the morning sun borning from the fields, but down in the dark earth deep it could feel the rich warm rays seeping through and through and it was stirring, more and more, stirring in the ground.

It could not see the spider stretch its legs along the roads of its sun-dancing web or the bug dreaming on the tip of the long green bough. It could not see, it could not see, yet now, all the time now, it lay stirring, stirring in the ground. 37

It could not see the butterfly with wings of black and gold dip and rise and dip again on the white and yellow flower sea, or hear the sound of the big fat bee buzzing round the clover plums. Still, still, it was stirring, stirring in the ground.

38

It could not smell the violet wood or the wind
that came across the sea... 39

It could not see the man, woodman, or hear the
crack-cracking ax. It could not see the
humming bird or the crow.
Then could it know?
      could it know . . .

40

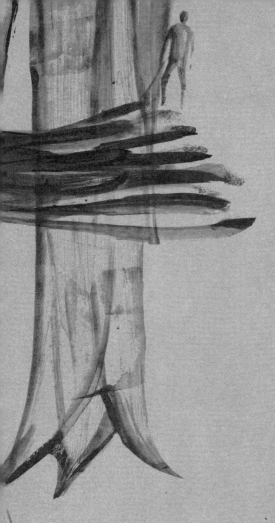

Dark seed silent as the snail crawling to the
edge of sea, it came upon that second evening
that it fell itself to dreaming:
Am I stone, dark earth?
stone to be...
make me see
what is this fire that burns,
burning always in me?

Glowing red like a star in the midnight earth,
the fiery flame within it burned and burned
until that night the moon all full and bright
did speak to it:
I have brought the sea
across the sky with me
and turned the lotus flower to
my star.
I have stirred the hills with moonwind and
wild mushrooms dance for me. Now come
little seed, come to me.

And the seed turned in the earth:
    Now I shall see
    Now I shall see.

It was not that night that the seed opened but on the third morning. And it came through the earth a dark violent little flower with purple petals and white as snow inside and it wanted to crow, oh, at last to crow...

But it was born under a leaf —
it could not see
born under a leaf
and it could not see...

44

GEORGE MENDOZA represents one of the most independent and unique talents to appear in a long time. He is the author of many acclaimed books for children and is the winner of a Lewis Carroll Shelf Award for *The Hunter I Might Have Been*. A native New Yorker, Mr. Mendoza attended the State University of New York Maritime College for two years and later received his B.A. degree from Columbia University. Having always lived near the sea, he learned to sail as a boy and has twice crossed the Atlantic Ocean on a small sloop from New York to England.

Among George Mendoza's twenty-five previously published books are: *A Piece of String; The Hawk Is Humming; Flowers and Grasses and Weeds; And Amedeo Asked, How Does One Become a Man?; The Sand Poems; To See a Train Go By; A Wart Snake in a Fig Tree; Fish in the Sky; Herman's Hat;* and *The World From My Window.*

ATI FORBERG, born in Germany, was educated there and in England, and, after coming to this country, attended the Institute of Design in Chicago. Mrs. Forberg is the mother of two young daughters, and the family currently lives in Brooklyn, New York.

Among the many children's books illustrated by Ati Forberg are: *Attic of the Wind; Magic Carousel; On a Grassgreen Horn;* and, for Funk & Wagnalls, *Where the Wind Blows.*